The Beacon Library

BOOK SIX STAGE

THE
BRONZE MIRROR
and other plays

BY
GLADYS STAINES
ILLUSTRATED BY PEARL FALCONER

GINN AND COMPANY LTD
LONDON & AYLESBURY

For permission to adapt and dramatise the stories in this book, grateful acknowledgement is made to the following authors and publishers: The Trustees for Miss Rhoda Power for "The Wooden Horse" adapted from *The Wooden Horse of Troy*; Wells Gardner Darton & Co. Ltd. for "The Seven Lanterns" from *The Seven Champions of Christendom* by F. J. Harvey Darton; Longmans Green & Co. Ltd. for an adaptation of *The Three Wonderful Beggars* by Andrew Lang; Penguin Books Ltd. for "Robin Hood and Sir Richard of Legh" adapted from *Robin Hood* by Roger Lancelyn Green; Thomas Nelson and Sons Ltd. for "The King's Punishment" from *Stories from William Morris*; Oxford University Press for "The Quest for Olwen" from *Welsh Legends and Folk Tales* by Gwyn Jones; J. M. Dent & Sons Ltd. for "The Bronze Mirror" adapted from *Virgil's Mirror* from *Minstrel Tales* by Sturt and Oakden.

GLADYS STAINES
1961
Fifth impression 1975   047511
Product No. 012165204   ISBN 0 602 20146 2

Published by Ginn and Company Ltd,
Elsinore House, Buckingham Street, Aylesbury, Bucks HP20 2NQ

Printed in Great Britain at the University Press, Oxford
by Vivian Ridler Printer to the University.

PREFACE

THESE plays have been written for children who, because they have mastered the mechanics of reading, are able to read with a marked degree of fluency. Such fluency is essential if the children are to derive pleasure from reading stories in dramatic form. To aid fluent reading it will be found that with the exceptions listed on page 4 all the words are familiar to children who have used the Beacon Readers.

While the plays can be acted in the classroom, this book is primarily a reading book and not one whose contents should necessarily be memorised. Ideally the plays should be read by small groups of children so that as many as possible take part.

Children who have passed through the Infant School are beginning to awaken to the spirit of adventure and they are eager for reading material which portrays deeds of heroism. They have also reached the age when they are ready to be introduced to stories which form part of their literary heritage. These two factors have governed the choice of the stories which are included in this book.

GLADYS STAINES

The only words in this book which may give difficulty to children who have read William Tell and have studied the Pronunciation Excercises at the end of that book (the main reader for the Book Six Stage of Beacon Reading) are listed here:

<table>
<tr><td>page 7
centuries</td><td>page 50
patiently</td></tr>
<tr><td>page 8
Ulysses</td><td>page 83
rogues</td></tr>
<tr><td>page 13
anchor</td><td>page 94
exhausted</td></tr>
<tr><td>page 14
assaults</td><td>page 107
ivory</td></tr>
<tr><td>page 15
persuade</td><td>page 123
Horatius</td></tr>
<tr><td>page 17
Rhodus</td><td>page 124
centurions</td></tr>
<tr><td>page 49
proves</td><td></td></tr>
</table>

CONTENTS

Many centuries ago there lived in the land of Greece a beautiful princess whose name was Helen. She was so beautiful that princes from far and wide wished to marry her.

One day Helen's father, Zeus, sent for his wife, Leda.

ZEUS   Wife, I hear that many mighty princes desire to marry our daughter, Helen.

LEDA   It is true, husband, that Helen has many suitors. Doubtless they would give all they possess to win her hand in marriage.

ZEUS   Yet, if I give Helen to any one of these princes I shall make enemies of those I refuse.

LEDA   If Helen's suitors were invited to Greece our daughter could choose for herself. You would then have refused none.

ZEUS	You speak wisely. Helen shall make her own choice. Steward!
STEWARD	Yes, sire?
ZEUS	Send messengers to the countries where the princes live ; to the islands and the hills ; to the mountains and the valleys. Then prepare a feast.
STEWARD	The feast shall be prepared, sire.

The messengers travelled swiftly bearing invitations to those who sought Helen's hand in marriage. Many princes came to Greece. Some rode on horses, some travelled in chariots, some came from over the sea in sailing ships.

Zeus received his guests one evening at sundown.

ZEUS	Princes, you are welcome to our. fair land of Greece. We have summoned you that our daughter, Helen, may choose the one she would wed.
PRINCES	We are glad, sire, that the choice is left to Helen.
ZEUS	Before I present my daughter to you there are two things you must promise.

8

The first is that you will never quarrel with the man whom Helen shall choose for her husband.

PRINCES   Zeus, we declare we will quarrel with no man. We will be content with Helen's choice.

ZEUS   The second thing you must promise is that you will come to the assistance of Helen's husband if ever he is in trouble.

PRINCES   We promise. We will help Helen's husband if trouble overtakes him.

ZEUS   Wife, bring forth our beloved daughter,

LEDA   Helen, go to your father.

ZEUS   Dear daughter, these noble princes have travelled far by land and water seeking your hand. To you I leave the choice of a husband.

As the princes waited in silence Helen stepped from her father's side and stood before Menelaus, King of Sparta.

HELEN   Father, I choose for my husband, Menelaus, King of Sparta.

ZEUS	Go, daughter. We send you forth to the land of Sparta as her queen.

So it came to pass that Helen went to live in Sparta as the wife of Menelaus.

Now far away across the sea there lived in the city of Troy a prince named Paris. One day his father, Priam, sent for him.

PRIAM	Son, I wish to send you on a journey across the sea to Sparta. Go, carry presents to Menelaus, King of Sparta and greet him in my name.
PARIS	Sire, I gladly obey your commands. I will visit King Menelaus and return within a year.

Paris set sail, and after voyaging for many days through stormy seas he reached Sparta. There he was greeted by King Menelaus.

MENELAUS	Welcome, Prince Paris, to the land of Sparta.
PARIS	Sire, I bring gifts from my father. I bring, too, his greetings.

MENELAUS   We are honoured that you have come, Prince Paris. While you remain in Sparta our palace shall be your home. Wife, bid this stranger welcome.

HELEN   Sir, I bid you welcome.

PARIS   Fair queen, I thank you for your kindness.

MENELAUS   I have soon to journey to a lonely island in a distant part of my kingdom. But I shall return before the winter storms begin. Prince Paris, I leave my wife, Helen, in your care. Guard her well. See that no harm befalls her.

11

PARIS   Sire, I will protect the queen with my
                 life.

Now Paris was not true to his word, and when
King Menelaus had sailed away the prince seized
Helen and carried her off to Troy. So it was that
when Menelaus returned to Sparta he found that
Helen had gone.

MENELAUS   Steward, summon the princes who, at
                 my marriage, promised to help me if I
                 was in trouble
STEWARD   Yes, sire.

Messengers travelled far and wide. Soon all the
princes, led by Ulysses, gathered together to fulfil
their promise.

MENELAUS   Princes, I thank you for coming. You
                 will remember that at my betrothal you
                 promised to help me if I was overtaken
                 by trouble.
                 The time has now come for you to
                 keep your promise.
ULYSSES   Tell us of your trouble, King Menelaus.

MENELAUS   While I journeyed to a remote island in my kingdom I left my wife in the care of Paris, Prince of Troy. On my return I found that he had betrayed his trust and carried Helen off to Troy.

AGAMEMNON   For shame, for shame. We will fight against Troy and bring Helen back to the shores of Sparta.

Agamemnon gathered together an army of one hundred thousand men. He appointed Sestus their commander. A thousand ships, with black sails, rode at anchor in the bay ready to carry the soldiers to fight against Priam, King of Troy.

For nine long years Troy was besieged, but its strong walls withstood all the attacks and assaults of the enemy. Inside the city the days passed slowly for Helen.

Sestus   For nine long weary years we have waged this war to rescue Helen, and still the walls of Troy stand firm. Our soldiers grow restless, and they long for home.

ULYSSES	I have devised a plan which will cause our enemies to be defeated, and which will bring us victory.
AGAMEMNON	Unfold your plan, Ulysses. We will consider it.
ULYSSES	We must make a hollow wooden horse large enough for several men to hide inside.
SESTUS	A hollow wooden horse! Ulysses, you must be mad. Whoever heard of a wooden horse winning a war?
ULYSSES	Listen, Sestus. You must pretend to withdraw our army by ordering the soldiers to embark. Then set sail in daylight, for we must deceive the Trojans. They must think we have abandoned the siege of Troy.
SESTUS	But what of the wooden horse?
ULYSSES	I, and some of our bravest soldiers, will conceal ourselves inside the horse. We will, in the meantime, send out a spy who will persuade the Trojans to drag the horse inside the city. When night falls

we will climb out of the horse and fling open the city gates that our army may enter. By this time you will have brought back our ships and disembarked our soldiers, ready for the assault.

AGAMEMNON Although your plan seems foolish, Ulysses, we will try it since all else has failed. The wooden horse shall be made.

The noise of hammering resounded through the Greek camp as the wooden horse took shape. Then the Greeks embarked and pretended to sail away.

Telamon and Rhodus, Trojan soldiers on sentry duty on the walls of Troy, watched the fleet sail.

RHODUS	So the Greeks sail for home!
	This is a great day for Troy.
TELAMON	We are delivered. We must hurry to King Priam with the news. There will be great rejoicing throughout the city.
RHODUS	Look, Telamon, the Greeks have left behind a wooden horse.
TELAMON	Come to the king without delay.

Calling another sentry to keep watch Telamon and Rhodus went to the palace of King Priam.

TELAMON	Sire, the Greeks have sailed for home.
RHODUS	And, sire, they have left behind a wooden horse.
PRIAM	You bring excellent news, soldiers. Now we shall have peace. The strong walls of our city have protected us from all the attacks of the enemy.
TELAMON	But what of the wooden horse, sire?
PRIAM	I will come and examine it for myself. But wait, who approaches?

As the king spoke, Simon, a Greek soldier came limping towards him.

SIMON	Sire, I am a poor Greek soldier left behind when my countrymen sailed for home.
PRIAM	Then perhaps you can enlighten me. What is the meaning of the wooden horse?
SIMON	That horse, sire, is of great value. Do not leave it outside the city gates.
PRIAM	Well, no harm will be done if it is brought inside.
	Sentries, tell the commander of my army to bring the wooden horse within the city walls.

The wooden horse was dragged through the city gates and left standing in the market square. That night, when all was still, Ulysses touched the spring which opened the door in the horse's side. The Greek soldiers, armed with spears, leaped out. Along the shore sailed the Greek ships returning to Troy under cover of darkness.

ULYSSES	Quick men, to the city gates.
	Open them that our army may enter.

TELAMON	Sound the alarm!
	Sound the alarm!
	The Greeks are on us.
ULYSSES	Surrender. Troy is ours.
	Bring out Helen, Queen of Sparta.

The Greek army rushed the gates of Troy and the city was taken. Helen was brought out to the market place where Menelaus stood waiting for her. Taking her hand he led her down to the shore from whence they set sail for Sparta.

So a city fell, and a queen was rescued, by a horse which could neither move nor speak.

Many hundreds of years ago a war broke out between Spain and her enemies. The commander of the Spanish army, Count William, was planning his campaign with his captain when a messenger arrived.

COUNT WILLIAM   What tidings do you bring, messenger, good or ill?

MESSENGER   Sir, the enemy gathers on the borders of our land while his ships encircle our coasts.

CAPTAIN   What is the strength of his army, and how many ships has he at sea?

MESSENGER   His army numbers ten thousand, and he has fifty ships, fully manned.

COUNT WILLIAM   So, we have no choice but to fight in defence of our land. Unfurl our flag and call every able-bodied man to fight for Spain. To-morrow we march.

CAPTAIN   We shall require horses too, sir.

Count William They shall be provided. Here, messenger, convey this letter to the Master of the Horse. Now, captain, go with all speed, and may success attend our arms.

Captain Farewell, sir. To-morrow we shall meet on the field of battle.

Now Count William had recently married a wife named Condesa. Her heart was full of sorrow when she saw her husband preparing for war.

Condesa Tell me, husband, how many months will you be absent from home?

Count William Dear wife, I cannot tell. But if many years pass and I do not return, count me dead.

Condesa Ah, dear husband! I would wait a lifetime for your homecoming.

Count William Dear wife, before I leave you take this ring of pure gold. Guard it well, and wear it always. By this shall you remember me.

Farewell, farewell.

Then Count William buckled on his armour, mounted his horse, and rode away to fight for Spain.

Four years passed, then six years, then ten years, but travellers and wayfarers passing the castle brought no news of the count.

Each day Condesa, attended by her ladies, watched for her husband from the castle walls.

CONDESA   Perhaps my husband will come to-day. Alas, alas! Shall I ever see him again?

1ST LADY   My lady, you sorrow as though your lord were dead. Be brave, for he may yet return unharmed.

CONDESA	Ten long weary years have passed since my lord rode away to battle. Yet I cannot believe that he is dead.
2ND LADY	Perhaps he fell in battle, and he is wounded, or perchance he is a prisoner.
CONDESA	I can remain here no longer. Order my horse to be saddled, and I will journey beyond the borders of our land, searching for my lord. See, I wear upon my finger the gold ring he gave me when we parted. By this token shall he know me.

So Condesa, riding a white horse, and accompanied by her squire, left the castle.

Count William still lived, but he was held captive by Rosina, a lady of great power and wealth. She refused to release the count unless he promised to marry her.

ROSINA My lord, why are you so mournful and heavy hearted?

COUNT WILLIAM I mourn and sigh for my lady wife. Oh, that my wish to see her again might be granted!

ROSINA But your wife will have become tired of waiting for your return. By now she will have married again, or maybe she is dead.

COUNT WILLIAM When we parted I gave my wife a ring of pure gold. Unless that ring is brought to me here I shall never believe that Condesa is dead.

One evening, as Count William and Rosina sat in the twilight, a white bird flew in at the lattice window and perched on the count's shoulder. Quickly Rosina stood behind his chair and slipped a ring of gold into the bird's beak.

COUNT WILLIAM Alas, alas! A white bird is always the forerunner of bad news. This bird comes to tell me of my wife's death.

ROSINA I fear the news is true, for look, Count William, this bird carries in its beak a beautiful gold ring. Is not this the ring of gold you gave your wife, before you left to fight for Spain?

COUNT WILLIAM Shew me the ring. It is the selfsame ring I gave Condesa, my dear wife. Then she is dead. It is too late.

All this time Condesa journeyed far and wide searching, searching, for her husband. One day, when she had almost given up all hope of finding him, she came upon a cowherd driving his cows out to pasture.

CONDESA   Tell me, good cowherd, whose cows are these?

COWHERD   They belong to the Lady Rosina. She commands all this fair land.

CONDESA   To whom does this ripe yellow wheat belong?

COWHERD   It belongs to the Lady Rosina too. It is she who ploughs and reaps in these fields.

CONDESA   And whose are these flocks of sheep with their young lambs?

COWHERD   These, too, belong to the Lady Rosina.

CONDESA   Whose splendid castle is this, cowherd? Who owns these beautiful gardens?

COWHERD   These also belong to the Lady Rosina.

27

While Condesa spoke with the cowherd she saw Count William ride out of the castle mounted upon a fine black horse. Rosina rode proudly at his side dressed in a scarlet gown, with gold in her hair.

CONDESA   Cowherd, tell me quickly, who is that splendid soldier, and the lady who rides so proudly by his side?

COWHERD   That is Count William and the Lady Rosina. They ride to their wedding. This very day at noon they are to be married in the church below the castle wall.

CONDESA   Quickly, cowherd, give me your cloak and take this gold for your trouble.

Condesa threw the cowherd's rough cloak round her shoulders. She pulled out her silken purse and gave him three pieces of gold. Then she threw her horse's bridle over a nearby gate. As Count William and Rosina passed she stood pretending to beg.

CONDESA   A penny, a penny, good sir.
                 Of your kindness a penny, fair lady.

Spare a penny for a poor old **beggar** woman.

COUNT WILLIAM Old beggar woman, you are a **stranger** here.

Yet your face is familiar.

From whence do you come?

CONDESA I have travelled many, many **miles** from my own country.

ROSINA My lord, we must hasten. It is almost noon, and our wedding bells peal out.

COUNT WILLIAM I must stop to question this old beggar woman. What brings you here?

CONDESA I travel searching everywhere for my husband. My search is ended, but it is too late for he is about to be married to another.

COUNT WILLIAM Where have you found your husband?

CONDESA Do you remember this ring?

ROSINA Come, my lord, the horses grow restive.

COUNT WILLIAM Condesa, this is the ring I gave you, my wife, when I rode off to battle ten years ago.

CONDESA I am still your own true wife, Count William. This ring which I wear I have guarded since the day you went.

COUNT WILLIAM Then the white bird which alighted on my shoulder carrying a gold ring in its beak was false. I have been most cruelly deceived.

Rosina, when she found that her plot had failed, fell from her horse in a swoon.

COUNT WILLIAM Page, summon help and carry the Lady Rosina back to her castle.

PAGE Yes, sir.

COUNT WILLIAM Come, my lady wife, mount your horse. We will escape while we may and return to Spain. But for your faithfulness I should have remained captive for ever in this foreign land.

CONDESA Did I not tell you, husband, that I would wait a lifetime for your return? I refused to believe that you were dead. I knew that one day I should find you again.

There was once a wizard named Lester who worked such wicked spells that those who entered his castle were doomed to sleep for a thousand years. Early one summer morning Saint George, Saint Denis, Saint Andrew and Saint Patrick, rode out to discover where Lester's castle stood. These four champions wished to break the wizard's power, and to rescue those who slept within the castle walls.

ST. GEORGE   Come Saint Denis, Saint Andrew and Saint Patrick, we will ride in search of Lester, the wizard.

ST. DENIS   I have heard that he lives in a castle built like a mighty fortress upon a hill.

ST. ANDREW   The castle is surrounded by a deep moat crossed by a drawbridge. Those who enter are never seen again.

ST. PATRICK   Look ahead, Saint George. Do you see those battlements against the sky? We must be near Lester's castle.

B

ST. GEORGE   Come, spur on your horses, for we must not delay.

Saint George and his companions galloped up to the castle, and stopped before the iron gates which led to the drawbridge.

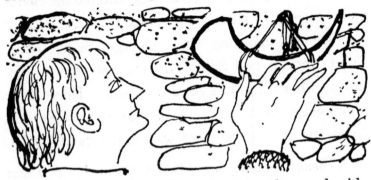

ST. GEORGE   A silver hunting horn hangs beside the gate. Go close, Saint Patrick, and read what is written upon the horn.

ST. PATRICK   " Sound me.

I open gates for all who dare.
But let the man who enters here,
Beware."

ST. GEORGE   Is there a champion in our company bold enough to sound the horn?

ST. ANDREW   I will sound it, Saint George.

St. Denis	No one answers the horn's call, but look, the drawbridge is lowered.
St. George	Forward, forward, over the drawbridge into Lester's castle.
St. Patrick	But we cannot pass beyond the drawbridge for the entrance is barred by a strong oaken gate.
St. George	And on the gate hangs a horn of ivory. Go, Saint Patrick, and read the message upon the horn.
St. Patrick	" Be warned in time, This is no place of peace."
St. George	Is any bold enough to sound this horn?
St. Denis	I will sound it, Saint George.

The oaken gate swung open as Saint Denis blew two piercing notes upon the ivory horn. But the way of escape was cut off for the drawbridge slowly rose. Suddenly a great darkness fell.

St. George	Come, grasp each others hands, for Lester has sent this darkness to separate us. We will move forward together until we find a wall.

35

ST. DENIS	A wall, a wall, my foot has touched a wall.
ST. ANDREW	And I have touched some stone steps.
ST. GEORGE	Drop hands and be prepared. Draw your swords. Daylight is returning. Follow me down this flight of steps.
ST. PATRICK	See, another door bars our way.
ST. ANDREW	It is neither locked nor bolted, for it yields as I press upon it.

Saint Andrew pushed the heavy door wide open. Saint George and his companions found themselves standing in an enormous hall lit by a hundred flaming torches. Round the hall were tables where many sat feasting. At the high table Lester was drinking a goblet of red wine.

ST. GEORGE	Who is lord of this castle? Which man is Lester, the wizard?
LESTER	I am Lester. By my magic art I felt your presence within my castle. I tried to separate you by casting a spell of darkness upon you. But you kept too close together. However, you shall not escape me now.
ST. GEORGE	We carry our swords.
LESTER	Below my castle there is a deep dark dungeon. There you shall sleep for a thousand years under my spell.
ST. GEORGE	We will fight. Forward Saint Denis, Saint Andrew and Saint Patrick.
ST. DENIS	Alas, alas, darkness descends again and I cannot see.
LESTER	Darkness falls at my command for I have worked a spell.
	Servants, escort these four men to the dungeon. Secure the doors and leave them. There they will sleep until I break the spell which binds them.

Saint George and his companions were forced to

surrender their swords. They were taken down into the cold dark dungeon where, overcome by a deep sleep, they sank to the ground. As Lester sat down again to continue feasting in the great hall a servant came in and spoke to him.

SERVANT   Master, other travellers are crossing
             the drawbridge.
LESTER   How many are there in the company?
SERVANT   I saw two champions, and between
             them there rides a lady of great beauty.

Saint Michael and Saint David, riding one each side of Christabel, a fair lady, crossed the drawbridge. They found their way to the great hall.

LESTER   Welcome to my castle.
ST. MICHAEL We come seeking Saint George and his
             three friends.
LESTER   They lie sleeping in my dungeon,
             doomed to remain there for a thousand
             years under my spell. Before long you
             will join them, for upon you, too, will I
             work my spell. But first satisfy your
             hunger and thirst after your journey.

Servant, bring food and wine. I will
return when these strangers are re-
freshed.

As the servant brought dishes of meat, and flagons
of wine, he whispered in Saint David's ear.

SERVANT   My master's power will be broken for
ever, if you can succeed in putting out
the seven lanterns with magic water
from the Dark Pool.

ST. DAVID   Where are the seven lanterns?

SERVANT   Go through the little door under the
gallery at the end of the hall. It is
opened by a secret spring hidden behind
a loose stone in the wall. On the further
side of the door you will find the lanterns.

ST. DAVID   And where is the Dark Pool?

SERVANT   It lies beyond the room where the
seven lanterns burn. Take this lady
with you, for the lanterns will only be
quenched if the water is sprinkled by
one who is fair. Take also this shining
copper bowl.

39

ST. DAVID   Will you come, Lady Christabel, on this adventure?

CHRISTABEL   Most gladly will I come if I may help to rescue those who sleep.

ST. DAVID   Come then, let us delay no longer.

ST. MICHAEL   I have found the secret spring behind the stone. Watch while I press it.

CHRISTABEL   The door swings open.

ST. DAVID   I will go through first. Walk between us, Lady Christabel, that we may be able to protect you from any hidden danger.

Saint Michael, Saint David and Lady Christabel, found themselves standing in a small room which had seven sides. Round the walls hung seven lanterns, suspended on heavy chains. In the middle of the room stood a pillar of dazzling white stone.

ST. MICHAEL   What are the words engraved upon that pillar?

CHRISTABEL   " Seven lanterns burn,
To guard the wizard's power."

ST. DAVID   Now we must search for the Dark Pool.   Follow me.

ST. MICHAEL   I see it ahead.   It is well named the Dark Pool, for its waters look black and forbidding.   It is guarded by hobgoblins who dance round and round its edge.

HOBGOBLINS   We dance, dance, dance,
To guard the Pool,
For this is magic water.

ST. DAVID   Come, cease your dance.   This lady wishes to fill the shining copper bowl with magic water.

HOBGOBLINS   Never, never, never.
We are here to guard the Pool,
For this is magic water.

CHRISTABEL   I see words engraved upon the wall.
" Let but one drop of blood
Touch the water,
And we are undone."

41

Without speaking Saint Michael drew his sword and pricked his left arm. There was a loud clap of thunder as a drop of blood touched the waters of the Dark Pool. The hobgoblins fell flat upon their faces.

| St. Michael | Hurry, hurry, Lady Christabel. Fill the copper bowl with magic water. |
| St. David | Now go quickly and sprinkle it upon the seven lanterns. |

Lady Christabel sprinkled a few drops of magic water upon each of the seven lanterns in turn. As she did so the lights were extinguished, and there was a great earthquake. The massive walls of the castle cracked from top to bottom. Lester's power was broken for ever.

Saint Michael and Saint David hastened to the dungeon.

St. David   Saint George, are you there?

St. George   I am here, with my three companions. There are many others with us.

St. Michael   Come out, come out, Saint George, for the wizard's power is broken.

St. David   Come to the great hall for there we will feast together to celebrate this day.

Led by Saint George a great procession of lords and ladies, knights and squires, came up out of the dungeon. For three days there was great rejoicing in Lester's hall. Then those who feasted crossed the drawbridge and rode away, never to return.

43

THE VALUE OF SALT

King Richard had three daughters whose names were Rose, Elizabeth and Margaret. One day, as he returned from hunting wild boar in the forest, the king ordered his page to fetch each of his daughters in turn. He wished to discover which one bore him the greatest love.

KING   Page, take my horse. Then go, summon my eldest daughter, the Lady Rose. I desire to speak with her. She walks on the south terrace.

PAGE   Yes, Your Majesty.

As he approached the Lady Rose the page bowed before her.

PAGE   Madam, the king is home from the hunt. He desires to speak with you.

ROSE   I will go to my father.

Attended by the page the Lady Rose went quickly along the terrace to the king's chamber.

45

ROSE	Dear father, what is your pleasure?
KING	I wish to know which of my three daughters bears me the greatest love. Therefore, since you are my eldest child I have sent for you first. How great is your love for me, my dear?
ROSE	Father, I love you as we love the bread which is served at your table each day.
KING	As I guessed the love you bear me is very great. Since we cannot exist without bread so you cannot exist without me. Be seated at my right hand upon this damask chair while I question your sisters.
	Page, go summon my second daughter, the Lady Elizabeth.
PAGE	Yes, Your Majesty.
ROSE	My sister does her needlework with her ladies in the great hall.

The page went to the great hall and bowed before the Lady Elizabeth. She sat sewing while one of her ladies-in-waiting played the lute.

PAGE	Madam, the king desires your presence.

46

ELIZABETH   So my father has returned safely from
             the hunt.

The Lady Elizabeth dropped her needle and,
attended by a lady-in-waiting, she entered the king's
chamber.

ELIZABETH   Dear father, I hasten to come at your
             bidding.
KING   Now daughter, answer me truly. What
             is the measure of your love for me?
ELIZABETH   I love you, dear father, as much as a
             goblet of rich red sparkling wine.

KING Your love for me appears to be less than that of your elder sister. However, I know we can scarcely live without wine. Be seated, daughter, upon my left hand while I question your younger sister.

Page, go summon my youngest daughter, the Lady Margaret.

PAGE Yes, Your Majesty.

ELIZABETH The Lady Margaret strolls on the battlements in the cool evening air.

The page climbed to the battlements and bowed before the Lady Margaret as he approached her.

PAGE Madam, the king is home from the hunt and summons you to his chamber.

The Lady Margaret ran quickly down the narrow winding steps which led from the castle battlements.

MARGARET   Dearest father, what is your pleasure?

KING   Tell me, dear daughter, with what can you compare your love for me?

MARGARET   I love you, dear father, with all my heart. Indeed, I love you as we love salt.

KING   You love me no more than you love salt! Salt is the cheapest, commonest, most worthless thing that appears on my table. Your answer proves that your love for me is weak and faint. You are banished from my presence for ever. Go, leave me, and never return.

MARGARET   Father, I implore you, do not banish me. I am devoted to you, and my greatest joy is to be in your company.

KING   Away with you to the northern turret of the castle. There you shall dwell in solitude without friends, or companions.

Now the Lady Margaret loved her father with all her heart. When she was banished from him she was overwhelmed with sorrow. The windows of the turret where she was imprisoned overlooked a court-yard. Here a fountain played, its waters leaping and dancing in the sunlight. Early each morning the cook came to the fountain to wash the fruit which he was preparing for the king's table.

MARGARET   Cook, cook, have pity on me for I am lonely in this dark gloomy turret.

COOK   Madam, I wish with all my heart that it lay within my power to give you your liberty. But if I helped you I should rouse the king's anger, and thereby endanger my own life.

MARGARET   But there is something that you can do to help me. Will you do it?

COOK   I am your servant to obey your commands.

MARGARET   When you prepare my father's dinner to-day leave out the salt.

COOK   Madam, I will gladly do as you ask. Nothing could be easier.

MARGARET   Thank you, cook. Now I will wait patiently until my father sends for me.

At noon that day the king and queen, with their courtiers, took their places at the table in the great hall. The king's minstrels played in the gallery while pages ran hither and thither carrying dishes of food.

KING   What is the meaning of this? The food
            put before me has neither taste nor flavour.
            Fetch that rascal, the cook, this instant.
            He shall answer for this with his head.

QUEEN   My lord, my lord. Do not be angry.

KING   I have cause to be angry. Even my
            favourite dish of goose, roast upon the
            spit, is ruined. Page, fetch the cook this
            minute. Bring the rascal before me.

So the cook was brought to the great hall. He
stood trembling before the angry king.

KING   Nothing on this table has taste or
            flavour. What is the meaning of it?

52

COOK	Your Majesty, I heard in the kitchen that you considered salt the commonest, cheapest thing that appears on your table, I did not, therefore, think it good enough to use when cooking Your Majesty's food. Hence, no salt was added to your dinner.
KING	Alas, now I understand why my youngest daughter compared her love for me with our love of salt. Alas, alas, I have wronged her and punished her most cruelly.
QUEEN	My lord, you can send for her.
KING	I have lost my daughter, for surely the love she bore me will have turned to hate.
QUEEN	My lord, you have but to summon our daughter from the turret.
KING	Rose, Elizabeth. Go, hasten, and bring your sister to me.

The two sisters ran through the castle until they reached the narrow winding staircase to the turret.

ROSE	Sister, sister, all is well.
ELIZABETH	Our father has sent us to fetch you. He is no longer angry with you. Come.

Taking their sister by the hand the Lady Rose and the Lady Elizabeth brought the Lady Margaret before the king. As she entered the room he stepped forward to meet her.

KING
Daughter, my beloved daughter, I am deeply grieved at the great wrong I have done you.

MARGARET
Dear father, there was no other way of expressing my love for you than by comparing it with our love of salt.

KING
Can you forgive me, Margaret, that I doubted your love, and that I punished you so sorely?

MARGARET
Dear father, I love you still with all my heart.

KING
Then come, and be seated with me. We will dine together when the cook has prepared a dinner cooked with salt.

King Richard placed the Lady Margaret in the seat of honour at his right hand. Then he ordered a large dish of salt to be placed in the centre of the table.

KING   Courtiers, this dish of salt is the most precious thing on my table. It shall be placed here every day so that none may forget its value.

Every day of the year, except one, a silver dish filled with salt was brought to the king's table. But on the first day of June, the Lady Margaret's birthday, the salt was placed in a dish of beaten gold in her honour.

Paul Falconer.

THE THREE WONDERFUL BEGGARS

There once lived a merchant who had an only daughter named Elsa. The merchant was known as " Mark the Rich ", for he possessed great wealth, but he was a miser.

One day three beggars came knocking on the door of Mark's fine house which stood in the town square.

MARK	Who stands knocking at my door?
1ST BEGGAR	We are three hungry beggars. Give us, we pray, a crust of bread to satisfy our hunger.
2ND BEGGAR	Give us shelter, for the night is bitter.
MARK	Begone, begone, before I unleash my hounds.
ELSA	Dear father, have mercy, for these poor beggar men are tired and hungry. Misfortune may overtake us if you refuse to help them. Give them lodging, I beg of you.

MARK	Very well, daughter, since you implore me they may stay; but only until daybreak. They must leave at cock crow.

That night, when all was quiet, Elsa overheard the beggars whispering together.

2ND BEGGAR	Is there any news?
3RD BEGGAR	Yes, I have had a message that in the neighbouring village a baby boy has been born this night.
2ND BEGGAR	What shall we name him?
1ST BEGGAR	We will name him Jonathan.
3RD BEGGAR	What shall we bestow upon him?
1ST BEGGAR	We will bestow upon him all the treasure of Mark the Rich. He is a greedy selfish man who deserves to lose his wealth.
2ND BEGGAR	Let us hasten then to visit this new-born child.

The next morning Elsa told her father of the conversation she had overheard in the night. Mark was angry, for he knew that Elsa had not been dreaming. So he drove over the frozen snow in his sledge to the neighbouring village, to visit the mayor.

MAYOR   Good morning, merchant. Your business must be urgent for you to come on such a bitter day.

MARK   Good morning, Mr. Mayor. I have come to enquire if a baby boy was born in your village last night.

MAYOR   Yes, a little son was born in the home of Ivan, a poor peasant. This is his seventh child.

MARK   What name is the infant to bear?

MAYOR   His parents call him Jonathan.

MARK   You know, Mr. Mayor, that I am a wealthy man. It is a constant grief to me that I do not possess a son to inherit my riches. I propose, therefore, to take this baby boy and to bring him up. Then when I die he shall be my heir.

MAYOR	I will send a messenger to fetch Ivan. He will be glad to seize this good fortune for his youngest son.

Ivan came to the mayor's house and a servant brought him into the parlour.

MAYOR	Come in, Ivan, come in. This visitor is a rich merchant who wishes to bring your youngest child up as his own son.
IVAN	Good morning, sir.
MARK	Now Ivan, I hear that you are a poor peasant with seven children. As I have no son I will take your baby and make him my heir.
IVAN	That is indeed kind of you, sir.
MARK	To add to the bargain I will give you a thousand crowns.
IVAN	Well, as the money would be useful you may have my son, although I know his mother will grieve for him.
MARK	Go then, and fetch the baby. Wrap him in this warm foxskin and lay him in my sledge.

Now on the journey home Mark lifted Jonathan out of the sledge and thrust him under a hedgerow. There he left the baby lying deserted in the frozen snow. Presently three merchants, who were on their way to sell their merchandise to Mark, passed that way. When they saw the baby they stopped, and picking him up, they took him with them.

MARK   Welcome, friends, to my house. But what treasure have you wrapped so carefully in that foxskin?

1ST MERCHANT   It is a young child whom we found lying under a hedgerow by the roadside. His cry is so pitiful for he is almost frozen.

MARK	He appears to be a strong healthy child. I will find a nurse for him.
3RD MERCHANT	We knew you would take pity on the baby if we brought him to you.

The following night was dark and moonless. At midnight Mark wrapped Jonathan up again in the foxskin and carried him down to the seashore. There he left him lying in a cleft amongst the rocks. As daylight returned some fishermen, who were spreading their nets out to dry, found the baby.

1ST FISHERMAN	Come quickly. See what I have found; a little baby, but a few days old, lying amongst the rocks.
2ND FISHERMAN	He will perish with the cold. Let me take him home. My wife will have pity on him.

So Jonathan was brought up in the fisherman's cottage. Years passed, and one day, as the fishermen were washing their nets, Mark drove past.

MARK	Good-day, fisherman.
2ND FISHERMAN	Good-day, sir.

MARK	That is a fine young man working for you. Is he your son?
2ND FISHERMAN	No sir, but he has been brought up as my son.
MARK	How did he first come to you?
2ND FISHERMAN	Some years ago, one morning at daybreak, we found a little baby lying abandoned on the rocks. His only covering was a foxskin. I carried him home to my wife, and he has lived with us since that day.
MARK	What is the young man's name?
2ND FISHERMAN	We call him Jonathan.
MARK	As he is so strong he shall work for me. He will soon make his fortune.
2ND FISHERMAN	I should be lonely and sad at heart if Jonathan went. But I will call him.

Hearing the call Jonathan dropped the net he was mending and came over to Mark's carriage.

MARK	Young man, come with me and make your fortune.

63

JONATHAN	Gladly will I come, for I have often longed for adventure.
MARK	Your first task will be to deliver this letter to my wife. My house stands in the town square.
JONATHAN	I will deliver the letter safely.

Jonathan bade farewell to the fishermen and, taking the letter, he went in search of Mark's house. Along the road he overtook the three beggars.

1ST BEGGAR	Hullo, Jonathan.
2ND BEGGAR	It is many years since last we saw you.
JONATHAN	When did you last see me?
3RD BEGGAR	When you were only a little new-born baby. Since that day we have protected you from all harm.
1ST BEGGAR	What is that in your hand?
JONATHAN	This is a letter which my new master, Mark the Merchant, has entrusted to me. I am to carry it to his wife.

2ND BEGGAR   Let us read the letter. Ho! Ho! Listen, friends. Mark writes instructing his wife to lock Jonathan in the cellar of his house. There he is to remain a prisoner.

2ND BEGGAR   We will soon alter that. Hand the letter to me, and I will blow the writing away.

3RD BEGGAR   And I will blow another message upon it. Listen while I read what the letter says now.

Dear wife,

When you receive this letter my daughter, Elsa, is to marry this young man immediately. His name is Jonathan.

                  Mark.

1ST BEGGAR   So you see, Jonathan, you are to be married to Mark's daughter.

Jonathan delivered the letter to the merchant's wife who prepared for the wedding. The very next day Jonathan and Elsa were married.

C   65

When Mark returned home and discovered what had happened he became mad with rage. In order to part Jonathan and Elsa he decided to send Jonathan on a journey to visit the Serpent King.

MARK I am going to send you on a journey to the world's end to visit the Serpent King. It is many years since I saw him. Take him this brazen bowl as a gift.

On the following morning as the sun rose Jonathan left home. As he walked through the woods he heard a voice calling.

JONATHAN Who calls? No one is in sight.

OAK TREE I called. I, who am the voice of the old oak tree. Tell me, young man, where are you going?

JONATHAN I am travelling to the world's end to visit the Serpent King.

OAK TREE When you reach the end of the world, and you meet the Serpent King, ask him this question. How much longer must the old oak tree stand in the wood? It is rotten to the roots.

JONATHAN   I will remember your question, oak tree. Wait patiently until I return with the answer.

Jonathan followed a winding path which eventually brought him to the bank of a river. Here a ferry-boat was waiting to take him across.

JONATHAN   Ferryman, please take me across the river.

FERRYMAN   Are you going far?

JONATHAN   I am on a journey to the world's end to visit the Serpent King.

FERRYMAN   Then remember me, and ask the Serpent King this question. Must the ferryman work much longer? For thirty years he has ferried backwards and forwards across the river.

JONATHAN   I will ask the Serpent King the answer to your question.

Soon Jonathan came to a green meadow. In the middle stood a splendid house with walls of white marble, and windows of crystal. Jonathan heard a voice calling softly. It was the voice of a willow tree.

WILLOW TREE   Beware, stranger, beware. Do not linger for your life is in danger.

JONATHAN   Thank you, willow tree, for warning me. But there are two questions I have promised to ask the Serpent King.

WILLOW TREE   It is not safe for you to ask questions of the Serpent King, for if you do so he will strike at you with his poisonous fangs. Whisper your questions to me

and when he comes to rest beneath
my shade I will ask him for you.

The willow tree listened while Jonathan repeated
the questions asked by the oak tree and the ferryman. Then he hid in some undergrowth near by as
the Serpent King glided slowly through the meadow.

SERPENT KING   I will rest beneath the willow tree.
It lulls me to sleep as the wind sighs
through its branches.

WILLOW TREE   Rest quietly, Serpent King, for I
have two questions to ask you.

SERPENT KING   What is the first question, willow
tree?

WILLOW TREE   How much longer must the old oak
tree stand in the woods, for it is
rotten to the roots?

SERPENT KING   It must stand until it is pushed over.
When it falls silver and gold, hidden
by Mark the Rich, will be found
amongst its twisted roots. What is
the second question, willow tree?

WILLOW TREE   How much longer must the old

ferryman go backwards and forwards across the river?

SERPENT KING   When the next traveller steps into the ferry-boat the ferryman must stay on the river bank. If he pushes the boat out into the river the traveller will be compelled to row to the other side. From that moment he will be doomed to ferry the boat for ever. Now I am weary. Do not trouble me with further questions.

WILLOW TREE   Sleep softly, Serpent King, beneath my shade.

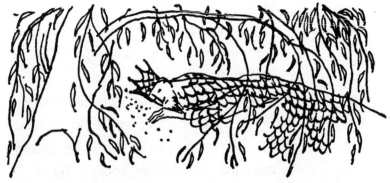

As the Serpent King fell asleep Jonathan crept away to the river where the ferryman waited.

FERRYMAN	Have you seen the Serpent King? Are my labours nearly over?
JONATHAN	Yes, I have seen him. I will tell you the answer to your question when you have ferried me across the river.

As the ferry-boat reached the other side Jonathan stepped out on to the bank.

JONATHAN	You will soon be at liberty, old ferryman. When the next traveller steps into the ferry-boat stay on the bank. Then push the boat out into the river with all your might. The traveller will be forced to row to the other side. From that moment there will be no escape for him. He will be doomed to ferry the boat for ever.
FERRYMAN	I shall not have long to wait, for already a traveller approaches.

The traveller who arrived was none other than Mark. As he stepped into the boat the ferryman gave it a mighty push out into the river.

FERRYMAN	At last, at last, I am free. You, sir, are doomed to take my place for ever.
MARK	Come, come, you cannot leave me stranded in your boat. I have scarcely strength to pull to the other side.

As Mark struggled to row the boat to the opposite bank Jonathan and the ferryman walked away, leaving him to his doom.

JONATHAN	Now I will find the hidden treasure amongst the roots of the old oak tree.

The oak tree stood waiting patiently for Jonathan's return.

JONATHAN	I have returned, oak tree, with news for you.
OAK TREE	Tell me quickly if my work is done. May I stretch out and rest?
JONATHAN	Yes, oak tree. The time has come for you to rest for ever. I have learnt that a great store of wealth lies hidden amongst your roots.

Gently Jonathan pushed the old oak tree over on to a mossy bank where it lay content to rest. Amongst its gnarled and twisted roots he found heaps of silver and gold. Hearing a voice he looked round. The three wonderful beggars stood watching.

1ST BEGGAR	The treasure is yours, Jonathan.
2ND BEGGAR	Go home to your wife, Elsa, for she watches for you.
3RD BEGGAR	May you both live peacefully and happily for many, many years.

So ends our play. Mark was punished for his greed and wickedness. The ferryman was released from toil. The old oak tree rested peacefully upon the mossy bank, while Jonathan and Elsa lived for many years to enjoy their wealth.

ROBIN HOOD AND SIR RICHARD OF LEA

One day Robin Hood sat with his band of merry men under a greenwood tree.

ROBIN HOOD   We will not dine this day until we are joined by a stranger. Little John, do you go through the greenwood searching for some traveller who will pay handsomely for his dinner.

LITTLE JOHN   I will hasten to do your bidding, Robin Hood.

ROBIN HOOD   Take your bow and arrows and see that you, and our unknown guest, return before the venison is cooked. We will dine from the deer which Will Scarlet shot yesterday.

Carrying his bow and arrows Little John went through the forest glade. Here he encountered a knight who rode his horse as though he was weighed down with many cares.

LITTLE JOHN	Good-day, sir knight. You look very weary and seem to be heavy hearted. Your horse is starved and thin.
KNIGHT	Good-day, forester. I have a heavy heart indeed.
LITTLE JOHN	Perhaps my master can assist you. Come, for he desires that some traveller dines with us this day.
KNIGHT	I am too troubled and too sorrowful to be good company for any man.
LITTLE JOHN	But my master is waiting dinner, and none dare disobey him.
KNIGHT	Pray, what is your master's name?
LITTLE JOHN	My master's name is Robin Hood. Come, follow me. With us you will find good fellowship and friends to help you.
KNIGHT	Alas! It is too late. Nothing can be done to help me. However, I will accompany you for I have heard much about Robin Hood.
LITTLE JOHN	This way, sir knight. Follow me through the greenwood.

Little John went ahead while the knight followed.

LITTLE JOHN   Robin, here is a gallant knight in sore trouble and distress.

ROBIN HOOD   Welcome, sir knight, to our forest home. You are indeed sorrowful. What troubles you?

KNIGHT   Sir Richard of Lea is my name. I am lord of Lea Castle beside the city of York. I have an only son who was betrothed to an earl's daughter, but this fair lady was stolen from him by another knight. In grief and anger my son killed his rival and I was obliged to pay a thousand pounds to save his life.

77

ROBIN HOOD   That was a large sum. How did you raise the money?

KNIGHT   I sold my lands, but that was not enough. I was compelled to borrow four hundred pounds from the abbot of Saint Mary's Abbey. The day approaches when I must settle my debt. But so great is my poverty that I possess only ten silver coins. If I do not repay the abbot by noon tomorrow he will seize my castle.

ROBIN HOOD   Have you no friends from whom you could borrow the money?

KNIGHT   When I had wealth I had friends. Now I am poor they have forsaken me.

ROBIN HOOD   I will lend you four hundred pounds for the space of one year. Count out four hundred pounds, Will Scarlet, for this brave knight.

WILL SCARLET   I will fetch the money bags, Robin Hood.

MUCH   Before Sir Richard visits the abbot of Saint Mary's Abbey cannot we provide him with new clothes, and a good horse, Robin Hood?

ROBIN HOOD   Yes, without doubt Sir Richard must be clothed as befits a knight. We will mount him, too, upon a noble horse. Fetch new clothes, Much, and you, Little John, bring my horse, Chestnut.

KNIGHT   Good Robin, I thank you. I will return, without fail, this day a year hence, and bring with me four hundred pounds.

Dressed in new clothes, and mounted upon Chestnut, Sir Richard of Lea rode boldly through the forest. He was no longer sad and dejected for he carried four hundred pounds in two strong leather wallets.

Now the lord abbot of Saint Mary's Abbey, with all his monks gathered around him, sat waiting the arrival of Sir Richard.

ABBOT   This is the appointed day when Sir Richard must either pay his debt, or I will seize his castle. However, I do not expect to see him. In his poverty he will never find four hundred pounds.

1ST MONK   If Sir Richard has not arrived in half an hour he will be too late. We shall then be able to take possession of Lea Castle.

ABBOT   We will wait till noon. We will not be guilty of doing Sir Richard an injustice.

As the great clock of Saint Mary's Abbey began striking twelve Sir Richard of Lea entered the room, and stood before the startled abbot.

ABBOT	So, Sir Richard, you have come.
KNIGHT	Lord abbot, I am here on the stroke of noon, as I promised.
ABBOT	Where is the money to pay your debt? I doubt if you have brought it.
KNIGHT	Here are your four hundred pounds, lord abbot. Take them. My castle at York will never be yours.

As the Abbey clock finished striking twelve Sir Richard threw the two wallets containing the money down on the oak table before the abbot.

ABBOT	Count the money.
2ND MONK	There are exactly four hundred pounds, lord abbot.
ABBOT	Go, Sir Richard. I shall long remember this day when I was cheated of your castle.
KNIGHT	Farewell, lord abbot.

A year passed and Robin Hood, and his band of merry men, waited in the greenwood for Sir Richard of Lea to return as he had promised.

LITTLE JOHN	Let us dine, for I can fast no longer.
ROBIN HOOD	No, we will not dine without Sir Richard. Will Scarlet and Much, **go** through the forest seeking him, for **he** will not fail to come.

So Will Scarlet and Much went through **the** forest seeking Sir Richard.

MUCH	Let us wait here, Will, **and watch** from behind this tree.

WILL SCARLET	Look, Much, here come two monks riding on white horses, accompanied by a band of servants.
MUCH	Halt, travellers, in my master's name. He bids you welcome.
1ST MONK	Who is your master?
WILL SCARLET	His name is Robin Hood.
2ND MONK	I have heard of Robin Hood. My heart is fearful. Come, brother, we must not linger.
MUCH	Robin Hood invites you to dine.
1ST MONK	Thank you, good sirs. But take this message to Robin Hood. Say, " We are honest men who have no dealings with rogues."
WILL SCARLET	Do not attempt to escape, or we shoot.

When the servants heard this threat they turned and fled through the forest, leaving the two monks at the mercy of Much and Will Scarlet. In silence they followed the two merry men to the place where Robin Hood was sitting.

ROBIN HOOD	Welcome, travellers, to our forest home.
1ST MONK	We are on a journey to the lord abbot of Saint Mary's Abbey. Our business is urgent, and we cannot stay.
ROBIN HOOD	Little John, serve these two travellers quickly with meat and wine. Bring a portion of the king's venison.
2ND MONK	I tell you, sir, we cannot stay.
ROBIN HOOD	Perhaps you have brought four hundred pounds instead of Sir Richard of Lea.
1ST MONK	We know nothing of four hundred pounds. We carry only a little money lest we should be attacked, and robbed, on our journey through the forest.
ROBIN HOOD	How much have you?
2ND MONK	We have barely twenty shillings between us.
ROBIN HOOD	Little John, search the saddle bags of these monks.
LITTLE JOHN	Look, Robin, here are handfuls of silver and gold.

ROBIN HOOD	Count it out, Little John.
LITTLE JOHN	There are four hundred pounds.
ROBIN HOOD	Then the lord abbot himself has paid the money owed by Sir Richard of Lea.
1ST MONK	Alas, alas! What will the abbot say when we arrive without the four hundred pounds? He will never believe that our saddle bags were opened and robbed.
ROBIN HOOD	Ride on now to Saint Mary's Abbey. Your load is lighter than when you came. Tell the lord abbot that no good comes from defrauding honest men.

The two monks had scarcely gone when Sir Richard came through the forest on Robin Hood's horse.

ROBIN HOOD   Welcome, Sir Richard.

But what brings you here?

KNIGHT   What brings me here! Have you forgotten that I promised to return with four hundred pounds to pay my debt of a year ago?

ROBIN HOOD   Sir Richard, your debt has just been paid by the lord abbot himself.

KNIGHT   But Robin Hood, that is not possible.

ROBIN HOOD   Listen, Sir Richard. Two monks from Saint Mary's Abbey came through the forest. Will Scarlet, and Much, waylaid them and brought them here to dine. When they came they had four hundred pounds; when they left they had nothing. So the lord abbot has settled the debt himself. Now, come to dinner. Will Scarlet, fetch venison and wine for Sir Richard.

So Sir Richard of Lea continued to live in his own castle. Many were the times when the lord abbot looked with envy upon its grey walls and turrets as he rode into the city of York.

Pearl Falconer.

THE KING'S PUNISHMENT

King John was a wealthy king who married a beautiful princess and made her his queen. Everyone loved the queen, but John was so proud and haughty that his people feared him instead of loving him.

One fine morning, in the month of May, John woke early, for he was to hunt in the royal forest.

JOHN	Where is that servant of mine?
PAGE	Here, sire.
JOHN	Hurry, boy, hurry, for to-day I hunt. Order the groom to saddle the horses.
PAGE	I will go to the stables at once, sire.

The groom brought the horses round to the courtyard, and the king, dressed in his hunting clothes, mounted his horse. Before the hands of the great palace clock pointed to the hour of eight,

John and his courtiers were far away hunting in the royal forest.

The king galloped so swiftly in the chase that he left his lords and nobles far behind. Presently he came to the bank of a broad river. As he dismounted he stood gazing into the water. The hot mid-day sun beat fiercely down upon him.

JOHN   Since I am wearied and heated with the chase I will refresh myself, and bathe in this cool water. I will tether my horse to the branch of this tree.

While John bathed a peasant crept stealthily through the bushes along the bank of the river. The king saw the peasant snatch his clothes from under the willow tree where he had left them.

JOHN   Stop, thief, stop.
            You are guilty of stealing the royal clothes of John, the king.

PEASANT   It does not matter to me who owns these clothes. I need some new

	ones, so I am taking yours. I will leave you my ragged coat in exchange.
JOHN	And a ragged coat it is indeed! Stop, thief, stop.
PEASANT	I will borrow your horse, too. He is a fine animal and will carry me swiftly. Be careful where you leave your clothes when you bathe again.
JOHN	I cannot return to my palace dressed as a beggar. I will try and find William, my gamekeeper, for his cottage lies somewhere nearby. Perhaps he will be able to lend me a horse and some clothing.

John found the gamekeeper's cottage which stood in a little clearing in a copse of hazel trees. The gamekeeper's wife was in the garden feeding her poultry when John appeared.

WIFE	Go along, old beggar man. We don't want beggars around here.

JOHN	But I am no beggar. I am John, your king. Surely you recognise me. Open the gate. I need food and clothing, and a good horse. Tell William his king desires his help.
WIFE	If your story is true then I must be dreaming. If I'm dreaming perhaps this gate is not real. In that case you can enter without me troubling to unlatch it.
JOHN	How dare you treat me, your king, like a rogue, or a beggar.

And John was so angry that he flung himself against the gate. As it was neither locked, nor bolted, it gave way before him and he stumbled into the cottage garden.

WIFE	Now see what my husband thinks of your wild story. Perhaps he will believe you.

John rushed past the gamekeeper's wife and went through the garden. There he found William busy fencing in his piece of land.

WILLIAM	What do you want, old beggar?
JOHN	William, I am in great trouble. A thief stole my clothes while I was bathing in the river. The only garment he left in exchange was this dirty ragged coat. I, John your king, ask your help. Give me clothing and a horse to carry me back to the royal palace.
WILLIAM	Poor fellow!
	Here, wrap yourself up in this old cloak. It is threadbare, but it is better than the coat you wear.

93

Now the gamekeeper's wife had followed John down the garden, and she heard what her husband said.

WIFE
Even your old cloak is too good for him, husband. You cannot afford to give it away.

WILLIAM
Leave him alone, wife.

The poor fellow imagines he is the king. Take him to our cottage. Give him meat and drink and send him on his way.

WIFE
Neither meat nor drink do I give to beggars.

JOHN
Take your hands off my shoulder. How dare you touch me. I tell you I am your king. One day you shall suffer for this.

But the gamekeeper's wife took John by the shoulder and pushed him roughly through the garden gate.

Now John was several miles from his palace, and darkness was falling as night approached. Exhausted by his wanderings he flung himself down under a hedge by the wayside where he fell into a deep sleep. Soon he was awakened by the glare of torches carried by soldiers who lighted Lord Percy, one of the king's own councillors, on his way to visit the sheriff.

JOHN   Well met, Lord Percy. Stay and help your king. I am in great trouble.

SERVANT   You impudent fellow! How dare you speak thus to my master?

LORD PERCY   Well, and what does this vagabond want?

JOHN   It is a dark moonless night, Lord Percy, and therefore you cannot see my face. Have the torches brought nearer. Then by their light you will see my face plainly.

LORD PERCY   I see your face well enough.

JOHN   But surely you recognise my voice? It is John, your king, who speaks.

LORD PERCY   Your words are the words of a madman. Here, take this silver coin and buy yourself food. You look half starved. But keep your distance from the city. If news of this wild talk reaches the king's ears you will find yourself a prisoner in the king's jail.

Proceed, torch bearers, to the sheriff's house.

John wandered on. The light of the torches grew gradually fainter. When daylight broke John had reached the gates of his own city. He watched the farmers coming in from the country to market their butter and eggs. One of the farmers stopped and spoke to him.

FARMER   You look tired and hungry, old beggar man. Here, take a drink of milk.

JOHN   Thank you, farmer. One day I will reward you for your kindness.

FARMER   Where are you going?

JOHN   I am on my way to the king's palace. If you will drive me there

I will pay you handsomely. What is your name, and where do you live?

FARMER

My name is Simon. I own a little farm, but alas, it is quickly falling into decay.

JOHN

It will be nothing to me to have your farm put in order, for my wealth is as great as that of the king.

FARMER

Your talk is wild and foolish. But climb into my cart, and I will drive you to the courtyard of the king's palace.

So John climbed into the farmer's cart and drove to the royal palace. As he entered the courtyard his way was barred by one of the palace servants dressed in purple livery.

SERVANT — Get out of here, old man. This is no place for beggars. It is the king's palace.

JOHN — But you are mistaken, for I am the king.

SERVANT — The king are you! You look like it, I must say, in that ragged old cloak. It so happens that at this moment the king is seated on his throne in the great hall.

JOHN — I am the true king. The throne belongs to me.

SERVANT — Come and see his majesty, the king.

Perhaps he will be able to decide which of us speaks the truth.

So John followed the servant into the hall of the palace where, seated upon the throne, he saw someone so like him that he might have been his own brother. Upon his head the stranger wore the royal crown, and in his right hand he held the royal sceptre. By his side sat the queen enthroned upon a chair covered with cloth of gold.

SERVANT   Your Majesty, this madman declares that he is king of this realm. I have brought him before you to convince him that he is sadly mistaken.

KING-OF-A-DAY	And who are you to imagine that you are king?
JOHN	Who am I! Why, yesterday it was I who occupied the throne. I was adorned in the royal robes. I am the true king.
KING-OF-A-DAY	Oh foolish man! You are greatly mistaken. It is I who am the rightful king. My soldiers shall lead you from my presence. But before I summon them we will ask the queen if she remembers you.

Now, madam, am I the king of this realm, or is this poor wretched man the rightful king? |
| QUEEN | My lord, you are without doubt the king. I have never before set eyes upon this upstart. |
| KING-OF-A-DAY | And you, noble lords of my court, whom do you say is your king? |

And the four and twenty nobles of the king's court exclaimed,

You, sire, are our true king.

100

KING-OF-A-DAY	Now, beggar man, you have heard for yourself what the queen and my nobles say. But since you seem a poor unhappy fellow I will be merciful in spite of your foolish boast. We will find work for you in the royal kitchens.
JOHN	I tell you I am the king. I will not work in my own kitchen.
KING-OF-A-DAY	Then go. Soldiers, seize this rogue and put him outside the city gates.

John was seized by two soldiers who dragged him away out of the palace, through the city gates and out into the countryside. There they left him to wander alone. In the distance John saw a hut where there lived an old hermit. He followed the path which led to the hermit's hut. Arriving there he rapped on the wooden door.

JOHN	Open, good hermit, open to John, your king.

When the hermit opened the door John was overjoyed to find that he was recognised.

HERMIT	Alas, Your Majesty! What has happened that you come in such clothes?
JOHN	You are the first to recognise me for I have been cast out of my kingdom.
HERMIT	Come in and rest, Your Majesty, while I prepare food to strengthen you.
JOHN	It seems that I have brought great suffering upon myself through my pride of heart. I am a stranger to my own servants. Even my wife, the

102

queen, does not own me. Another king sits upon my throne and wears my crown, and the royal robes.

After the hermit had given John food and drink he lent him his own ass to carry him back to the palace. As John approached the city gates he noticed the gatekeepers whispering together.

1ST GATEKEEPER   It is without doubt the king.

2ND GATEKEEPER   Look, he wears old clothes, and instead of being mounted upon a horse he rides an ass. How strange!

As John rode through the streets he noticed how the people stood about whispering, and pointing, as they watched him pass.

When he reached the palace one of his soldiers greeted him.

SOLDIER   We are glad to see you home again, Your Majesty. The queen awaits. you in the parlour.

John entered the parlour and found the queen fallen asleep over her sewing. By her side stood the king-of-a-day. As John stepped toward him the king-of-a-day changed into an angel.

ANGEL
Do not be afraid. I was sent to reign as king instead of you for a whole day because you were proud of heart. Now you have learnt to be humble you may take your place again upon the throne. I bid you farewell. My work is done.

And the angel vanished as the queen awoke from her sleep. She spoke to John.

QUEEN
My lord, your nobles await you in the great hall. Come, take your crown and your royal robes, for you have long been absent.

JOHN
Indeed, dear wife, I have travelled far since last you saw me. I have returned to win my people's love. Come, for all is ready.

Taking the queen's hand John led her into the great hall to feast with his four and twenty nobles.

104

No one there except the king knew that the king-of-a-day had reigned in his place. But each of the nobles noticed that John was no longer proud and haughty. He reigned happily in his kingdom for many years. Instead of fearing him his people learnt to love him, and to serve him with willing hearts.

Culham, the warrior, wearing a mantle of purple silk rode out one morning on his black charger. He carried a buckler of ivory, and from his side hung a gold-hilted sword. He rode in search of Olwen, daughter of Giant Gundry, for he wanted her for his bride. Passing a wicket gate Culham drew rein and called to the porter.

CULHAM   Ho, there! Is there a porter at this gate?

PORTER   What brings you here?
What is your business?

CULHAM   Open the gate that I may enter.

PORTER   I will not open to you.

CULHAM   Open I say. If you refuse I will give three mighty shouts which will echo through your master's hall.

PORTER   Bawl your head off, if you please, but you shall not enter until I have spoken with Arthur, my lord.

The porter went within and spoke with Arthur while Culham waited impatiently without.

ARTHUR   What news, porter?

PORTER   There stands at the gate a stranger who demands entrance.

ARTHUR   Shall we give him entrance, Merlin?

MERLIN   My lord, give him entrance. He may bring important news from afar.

ARTHUR   Then we will speak with him.

Go, porter, open the gate and admit this stranger. Let him be served with food and drink. Garth, draw a horn of wine.

The porter lifted the wooden latch and opened the wicket gate. Without dismounting Culham rode into the hall and drew rein before Arthur.

ARTHUR   Dismount, friend, for you must be wearied with your journey. Take food and drink.

GARTH   Here, stranger, drink this horn of red wine. It will strengthen you.

CULHAM   I thank you, sir, for your kindness.

ARTHUR	What is your name?
CULHAM	My name is Culham. I cannot linger for I come seeking Olwen, daughter of Giant Gundry.
ARTHUR	Olwen does not dwell here.
CULHAM	Tell me where I can find her, for Olwen shall be my bride, and no other.
ARTHUR	Olwen dwells with her father in his fortress. There he guards her night and day.
CULHAM	Then I will journey on in search of Giant Gundry's fort.
ARTHUR	Do not venture to go alone, Culham. Garth and Mollen shall accompany you. They will be good friends if you stand in need, or if danger threatens you.
CULHAM	I thank you, Arthur. I am ready to start without further delay.

So it came to pass that Culham, accompanied by Garth and Mollen, rode through the wicket gate in search of Olwen. After journeying for three days they came upon an old shepherd tending his flock of sheep and lambs.

CULHAM	Come, let us draw rein and speak with this shepherd. He may be able to direct us to the giant's fortress.
MOLLEN	Good-day, shepherd. Do things prosper with you?
SHEPHERD	Things go well, sir. I tend this fine flock, and there is plenty of good pasture.
GARTH	Whose sheep are these, shepherd?
SHEPHERD	They are owned by Giant Gundry. Over yonder is his fortress. But what is your business, sir? It is not safe to remain on Giant Gundry's ground. He slays any who dare approach him.
CULHAM	We come searching for Olwen, the giant's daughter. Does she dwell within the fortress?
SHEPHERD	Oh, sir, do not venture near. Escape while there is time. Do not tarry or disaster will overtake you.
CULHAM	And why should we not seek Olwen?
SHEPHERD	Many have come looking, but none have found her. Go, sirs, go, I implore you, or you will lose your lives.

GARTH	We will not leave until we have seen Olwen.
SHEPHERD	Then come secretly to my cottage to-night, for Olwen visits my wife when the moon is full. On those nights the giant falls into a sleep so deep that it is safe for Olwen to leave the fortress.
CULHAM	Thank you, shepherd. We will come to-night when the moon is up.

That night, as the frost sparkled on the ground in the moonlight, Culham, Garth and Mollen, knocked softly on the cottage door. When the shepherd opened it they saw Olwen sitting by the fire. She was wearing a silken robe, and round her neck she wore a collar of rubies and pearls.

111

CULHAM	This is the maiden I seek.
	Come away, Olwen, come away with me and be my bride.
OLWEN	I have promised my father never to leave him. But if you are bold enough to ask for my hand my father will demand three hard things of you.
GARTH	If we succeed in doing these hard things, what then?
OLWEN	Then my father will be forced to let me go. On the day that I leave him he is doomed to become a dwarf.
MOLLEN	Take us to your father. We will speak with him.
OLWEN	Wait until daybreak and I will show you the way.

At daybreak, when the sun was rising, Olwen took Culham and his companions to her father's fortress.

OLWEN	Father, I have brought three travellers who wish to see you.
GUNDRY	And why do they trouble me? Begone, sirs, before I cut off your heads.

112

CULHAM	I come seeking the hand of your daughter, Olwen.
GUNDRY	No man takes my daughter from me. Begone, I say, begone.

As Culham, Garth and Mollen, turned to leave, the giant snatched a spear and hurled it after them. But Mollen caught it and threw it with such force and skill that it pierced the giant's knee.

The following day the three friends returned.

OLWEN	Father, the travellers have returned.
GUNDRY	Bring them before me. This time I will cut off their heads.
CULHAM	We have returned, Giant Gundry, for your daughter.

GUNDRY	Those who seek to win Olwen must do three things. But they are so difficult that they are almost impossible to perform.
MOLLEN	Tell us of these impossible tasks.
GUNDRY	Here is the first. You must secure Knock's sword. He is the giant who lives in a cavern on the mountainside.
GARTH	And what is the second task?
GUNDRY	A long time ago I possessed a bag full of flax seed. It must be found and the seed planted to grow flax for Olwen's wedding veil.
CULHAM	And what is the third task?
GUNDRY	On Olwen's wedding day the guests must eat from the hamper which belongs to Giant Long-Shank. But you will be unable to snatch it from him, for he guards it closely.
CULHAM	These tasks do not alarm us, Giant Gundry.

The first task took Culham, Garth and Mollen, to the mountain where Knock, the giant, lived.

114

On the way they overtook the giant's servant.

CULHAM   Is this the mountain where Giant Knock has his home?

SERVANT   Yes, but none who enter the cavern where my master lives leave it alive.

GARTH   Come, take us to your master for we would speak with him.

The giant's servant led Culham, Garth, and Mollen, through a long dark winding tunnel into the cavern where Knock sat gnashing his teeth.

KNOCK   Ho, there! Who gave you permission to enter my stronghold?

CULHAM   We have travelled far to speak with you.

KNOCK	I have no time for speech. Be off before I thrust my sword through your heart. Servant, hand me my sword.
SERVANT	Here it is, master.
MOLLEN	Giant Knock, your sword does not shine as it should. It is dull and tarnished. Let me polish it for you.
KNOCK	Are you skilled in polishing swords?
CULHAM	Mollen is so skilled that he is able to polish swords until they flash in the sunlight.
KNOCK	Then take my sword and polish it.

Mollen took a whetstone from under his cloak and cleaned one side of the blade.

MOLLEN	Does that please you, Giant Knock?
KNOCK	Splendid, splendid. Now clean the other side of the blade for me.
MOLLEN	I think your scabbard has damaged your sword. Hand it to me and I will mend it.

Mollen stood with the sword in one hand and the scabbard in the other. Followed by Culham and

Garth he rushed from the cavern carrying the sword, and the scabbard.

CULHAM Away, away, before Knock follows.

So the first task was finished. The second task was to find the bag of flax seed.

GARTH Stop, stop. Listen, what do I hear? It sounds like some one wailing and lamenting.

CULHAM Look, we are passing an ant-hill glowing with fire. We hear the ants crying and wailing for fear of death. Take Knock's sword, Mollen, and save them.

Mollen drew the giant's sword and cut the fiery patch from the ant-hill.

GARTH See, one ant is lame and cannot escape the fire. I will lift him to safety.

ANT Thank you, kind friend. You have saved my life indeed. As a reward you shall be granted one wish.

GARTH I wish to find the flax seed once possessed by Giant Gundry.

ANT   Return at midnight and the seed will be ready for you.

At midnight Culham, Garth and Mollen, returned to the ant-hill. An army of ants, each carrying a seed of flax, came up from below the ground.

ANT   Here is the flax seed you desired. Guard it well, for we cannot perform this marvel a second time.

GARTH   We thank you for your help. This seed is needed to grow flax for the weaving of Olwen's wedding veil.

118

CULHAM	Now for our third task we must seize the hamper belonging to Giant Long-Shank.
MOLLEN	Men say the giant eats from his hamper each noonday in the Forest of Dean.
CULHAM	Then we will ride to the forest.

Culham and his companions galloped along the highways until the following day at noon they reached the edge of the Forest of Dean.

CULHAM	Come, Garth and Mollen, let us tether our horses and creep quietly through the forest until we encounter Giant Long-Shank.
MOLLEN	Look, look, through the trees down the glade. There is the giant reclining by his hamper.
CULHAM	Tread softly, lest we disturb him. We must catch him unawares.
LONG-SHANK	Now I feel well satisfied and ready for sleep. I shall waken if a thief tries to steal my hamper.

CULHAM Garth, go quickly, and gather a handful of those purple flowers growing on the bank over there.

Garth picked a few purple flowers and brought them to Culham.

CULHAM Now hold the flowers beneath Giant Long-Shank's nose. The scent will make him sleep for ever and a day. Quickly, Mollen, help me carry the hamper. Take the other handle.

While Giant Long-Shank slept and snored the three friends galloped back to Giant Gundry's fortress with Knock's sword, the flax seed, and Giant Long-Shank's hamper.

CULHAM We have returned, Giant Gundry, with the three tasks completed.

MOLLEN Here is Knock's sword.

GARTH Here is the flax seed.

CULHAM Here is Giant Long-Shank's hamper.

Giant Gundry shook his fists, and instantly he shrank to the size of a dwarf.

120

GUNDRY   Alas, alas! I am forced to release my daughter, Olwen. Take her, she is yours.

So Culham took Olwen's hand and led her away. The next day they were married in the presence of Garth and Mollen. Then Culham took his bride to live far away in a splendid mansion by the sea. Garth and Mollen returned to Arthur's court where they recounted the adventures which had befallen them. Loud was the praise which greeted their story of prowess.

THE BRONZE MIRROR

There was once a time when the people of Rome lived in fear of being invaded by the people of Carthage whose armies were commanded by Hannibal.

Now there dwelt in Rome a citizen named Horatius who was renowned for his wisdom and courage.

One day Horatius sought an audience of the commander of the Roman armies.

SOLDIER   Sir, the citizen Horatius desires to see you.

COMMANDER   Bring him before me.

Bowing low Horatius entered the chamber where the commander sat taking counsel with his centurions.

COMMANDER   Speak, Horatius, and tell us what brings you here.

HORATIUS   Sir, I know well the dangers which beset our beautiful city of Rome. I have a plan whereby we can detect the approach of our enemies, before they reach the city gates.

COMMANDER   Soldier, summon the city fathers who wait without. We desire them to hear this wise man unfold his plan.

SOLDIER   City fathers, the commander of our armies wishes to speak with you.

Walking in solemn procession the city fathers came before the commander and his centurions.

COMMANDER	Pray sirs, be seated. Horatius is here to tell us how we may protect the citizens of Rome against attacks from our enemies.
	You may proceed, Horatius.
HORATIUS	We must make a huge mirror of bronze and erect it on pillars of marble by the northern gate of the city.
1ST CITY FATHER	How can a mirror protect our city?
HORATIUS	If our enemies march on Rome they will be reflected upon the surface of the mirror. Thus shall we be warned in time, and we shall be prepared for their attack.
2ND CITY FATHER	But the enemy will be upon us before we have time to arm.
HORATIUS	The mirror will be so bright that it will reflect the enemy while he is still thirty miles away. Thus shall we have sufficient time to arm.
COMMANDER	City fathers, you have heard Horatius speak. What say you?

3RD CITY FATHER   Sir, we advise you to order the mirror to be made without delay.

1ST CITY FATHER   It is indeed an excellent idea.

So a mirror of bronze was made while marble was quarried from the hills surrounding Rome. When the pillars had been made and polished they were erected at the gate on the north side of the city. Then, in the presence of the city fathers, and all the citizens of Rome, the great mirror of bronze was set up on the marble pillars.

Now there mingled with the crowd who watched a spy, named Adrian, who had been sent from Carthage by Hannibal. Unnoticed Adrian slipped through the city gate to his own country.

HANNIBAL   Our servant, Adrian, has been away for many months. We trust that no harm has befallen him.

SOLDIER   Sir, here is news. Adrian rode post-haste into the courtyard but a few minutes ago.

HANNIBAL   Bring him before me that I, and my generals, may hear of his adventures.

Adrian was summoned to appear before Hannibal.

HANNIBAL   Well, Adrian, what news do you bring of our enemies?

ADRIAN   Sir, I have come straight from Rome. There a great mirror of bronze has been set up upon pillars of marble by the northern gate of the city.

HANNIBAL   How does that concern us?

ADRIAN	Sir, the mirror is so large and bright that it will reflect our soldiers while they are still thirty miles from the city.
HANNIBAL	So, the Romans hope to be warned of our approach. We must, therefore, destroy the mirror before we can attack. Generals, how shall this be accomplished?
GENERAL	There is living in Rome a rich man who will do anything to gain more wealth. His name is Silius.
	Send three men to Rome dressed as merchants. Provide them with chests full of treasure. These they must bury when they reach Rome. Then they must visit Silius and tell him that much treasure lies hidden in the city.
HANNIBAL	How will this plot destroy the mirror?
GENERAL	The men you send must make Silius believe that some of the

treasure lies hidden beneath the mirror. His greed will cause him to search for it even there.

HANNIBAL   Well, we can but try.

The next morning three men named Hanno, Simon and Rustus, left Carthage dressed as wealthy merchants. They carried with them chests full of treasure. Arriving in Rome, under cover of darkness, they quickly buried the chests below the ground.

The following day, dressed in their finest clothes, they went to visit Silius.

SERVANT	Three strangers from afar desire to see you, master. They bear important news.
SILIUS	Bring them before me.

So Hanno, Simon and Rustus, appeared before Silius.

SILIUS	What news do you bring?
HANNO	Sir, we are wise men from a far country. Each night as we sleep many things are revealed to us through our dreams. We learnt last

night that under the city of Rome much gold is hidden.

SILIUS   There is gold beneath the city, and I know not of it! Good sirs, tell me where the gold is hidden. You must come and lodge here in my house.

Command what you will, but tell me where the gold is hidden.

SIMON   We will try and discover through our dreams this night where the treasure is to be found.

The next morning Hanno, Simon and Rustus, again appeared before Silius.

SIMON   Sir, I dreamed last night that treasure lies buried beneath the arch which spans the road before your house.

RUSTUS   And I dreamed that treasure lies buried in the market place below the fountain.

SILIUS   Summon the workmen. Go with them Hanno, Simon and Rustus.

131

Show them where to dig. Bring much gold and treasure and you shall share it with me. Go, with all speed.

Hanno, Simon and Rustus, guided the workmen to the places where they had buried the chests. Soon hoards of gold and precious stones were uncovered. Great was the joy of the greedy Silius when the treasure was brought before him.

The following day Hanno came before Silius again.

HANNO	I dreamed last night of more treasure buried in the city. If you discover it you will be the richest man in Rome.
SILIUS	Good Hanno, tell me your dreams that I may lay hands upon the treasure of which you speak.
HANNO	Not only is there gold, but in my dream I saw heaps of precious jewels which glittered and shone as though lit by a thousand lamps.
SILIUS	No matter where the treasure is hidden it shall be mine. Where can I find it?
HANNO	This wealth lies beneath the great mirror of bronze which is by the northern gate.
	I see you start. But have no fear. We will dig for the treasure without damaging the mirror.
SILIUS	Work speedily, for I am anxious to feel the jewels and precious stones between my fingers.

So accompanied by a band of workmen Hanno led the way to the great mirror. Throughout that day the men toiled without rest as they dug round the pillars of marble. When darkness fell Hanno dismissed them telling them to return early the following morning.

That night when Rome was quiet Hanno, Simon and Rustus, crept towards the mirror.

HANNO   See, Simon and Rustus, the pillars of marble are no longer safe for the workmen have dug well. We have but to push and the pillars will fall, taking the mirror of bronze with them.

So Hanno, Simon and Rustus, pushed with all their might. As the pillars crashed the mirror of bronze fell with a clang which resounded through the dark night.

Hanno, Simon and Rustus, crept silently through the city gate and, springing upon horses which were waiting for them, they set off swiftly back to Carthage.

Great was the rejoicing amongst the citizens of Carthage when they heard that the mirror of bronze had been destroyed. But great was the dismay amongst the citizens of Rome when they found how they had been betrayed by the greed of one man.

RING UP THE CURTAIN!

When a stage play has ended and the whole company of players has made their bow to the audience, a bell rings, the curtain is lowered, and the audience departs. Why, then, did we not head this page 'Ring down the curtain!' since you have reached the end of this book of plays? Because we have an idea.

Why not write a play yourself? Perhaps you cannot think of a good story to turn into a play. Ask your teacher to give you another book from The Beacon Library — *The Lion and the Saint* is a good one. There are several stories in that book out of which you could make plays, but the easiest one to begin with is *The Friar who was an Ass*. Start in this way:

Two friars, Brother Anthony who is very pale and thin and solemn, and Brother Timothy, who is red-faced, fat and jolly are walking towards their monastery one very hot afternoon carrying heavy loads on their backs.

Brother Timothy. Oh dear, how hot I am! How heavy my load is! Do let us sit down and rest.

Brother Anthony. Shame on you, Brother Timothy! Only a sluggard would make such a suggestion. Courage is all you need.

Brother Timothy. How hard and unfeeling you are, but (peering before him) Providence is more kind. For unless my eyes deceive me, I see an ass tied to a tree. He will carry our burdens for us.

Now read the story, continue the play, and

RING UP THE CURTAIN!